THE NEURODIVERGENTS
AUTISM

Real experiences of autistic children

BY I.M. ORKWERD

ALL 4 BOOKS IN ONE

Published in 2022 by
Ballads & Bards Bookhouse

Ballads & Bards Bookhouse
Wonnarua Country
AUSTRALIA
www.balladsandbardsbookhouse.com

A catalogue record of this work is available from the National Library of Australia

The Neurodivergents: Autism
ISBN: 978 0 6454389 2 5 (paperback)

10 9 8 7 6 5 4 3 2 1

Illustrator
Rhododendron Art
Text Design
C.A.Watts
Editor
C.A.Watts

Printed by Ingram Spark, an Ingram Industries company, and Kindle Direct Printing, an Amazon company.

Ballads & Bards Bookhouse acknowledges the Traditional Owners of the country on which we work, the Wonnarua and Awabakal nations, and recognises their continuing connection to their land, waters and culture. We pay respects to their Elders past, present and emerging.

This book belongs to

Samantha

McIntosh

THE NEURODIVERGENTS
AUTISM
AND RELATIONSHIPS

Real experiences of autistic children

WRITTEN BY- I.M.ORKWERD

Zuri

Dedicated to V,
My original therapy buddy.
I love you.

My name is Zuri
and I'm Autistic.

That means I don't connect
with people the same
way others do.

1

Autistic people often only have a few
things that they really like.

I love animals...

...and space!

I love them so much people can get frustrated
and say I don't talk about anything else. Unless
they love those things too!

When I get really interested in something, I have to know EVERYTHING. Like when I learned that Pluto wasn't a planet anymore and I started exploring space for the first time...

This urge to keep doing something once I've discovered I like it, is called

HYPERFOCUS.

I don't mind my hyperfocus, because I end up spending a lot of time doing things I love! But...

...it can make it hard to stop, even when someone wants me to do something else. Chores, school work, being introduced to someone new... All I can think is that I have to

FINISH FIRST!!!

Repetition is when you say or do something over and over again. I make the same noises over and over without realising I'm even doing it...

...and if I hear something funny, I'll repeat it. This is called

ECHOLALIA.

Teachers tell me to stop because it's distracting and other kids think it's annoying. I don't mean to be...

I can get in trouble for things I've said.
People say I have no filter. Whatever I think just
comes out of my mouth without thinking if it's ok.

We learn what we can and can't say by watching
people as we grow up. But people STILL get angry or
upset with me when I say something that I've
heard OTHER people say. I don't understand why it's
ok for them but not me?

How do you tell which things only certain people can talk about and which things **EVERYONE** can talk about?

People can worry about how they look, so it's best not to talk about it.

Why is it ok to say things at one time but not another?

And why don't people like scars? Some of the best stories I have are about how I got mine!

Once, I told my sister the way she smiled make her look like a duck. People got REALLY mad.

My family said
I called her ugly, but I never said that AT ALL! I was just describing what I saw. I feel like people think I'm being mean and doing it on purpose, but it's just not true. I don't ever want to hurt people...

My friends were easy to connect with because we loved the same things... and I never have to worry about being annoying or saying the wrong thing to them, because nobody knows people like us the way WE do!

Autism isn't an illness. My brain just works differently. I am Autistic. I am me. I am Zuri.

THE NEURODIVERGENTS
AUTISM
AND COMMUNICATION

Real experiences of autistic children

WRITTEN BY- I.M.ORKWERD

Mark

Dedicated to the real Mark,
Whose story keeps me strong when I'm weak.
If you can do it... we all can.
You got this.

My name is Mark
and I'm Autistic.

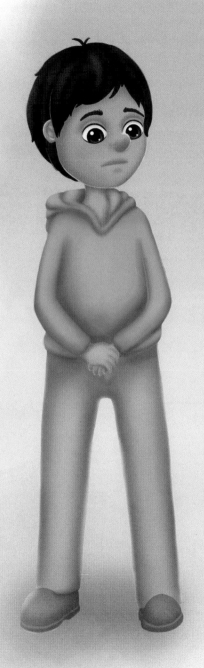

That means that
I don't communicate with
others the same way most
people do.

1

When people send a message with their body instead of saying it out loud, it's called a

SOCIAL CUE.

They could have a look on their face...

...or be standing a certain way...
but because they're not TELLING
me what their message is, I can sometimes miss it.

This can make it hard to make friends, because when I miss a social cue, I'm missing part of what they're trying to tell me.

That can hurt their feelings because it makes it seem like I'm not listening, even when I am.

3

It's also really confusing when someone says one thing...

Do you have anything to eat?

Oh, you're hungry? There's plenty of food!

...but mean something else.

Like when someone asked to use the bathroom. I said "Sure!"

Then they asked

"Well, are you going to tell me where it is?"

If he wanted to know where it was... WHY didn't he just ask in the first place?

5

It's good when people say exactly what they mean, so I don't have to look for sneaky hidden messages and get confused trying to find them...

...and it's MUCH easier talking to people when they know not to look for hidden messages in MY words.

There are times when people will tell me

"YOU DON'T SEEM AUTISTIC!"

But I am... and it hurts when people say that, because it sounds like

"LUCKY IT'S NOT OBVIOUS!"

If I don't SEEM Autistic it's probably because I don't feel comfortable enough to relax.

It makes me feel like being Autistic isn't ok.

People will tell me they have social issues too, or that

"EVERYONE IS A
LITTLE AUTISTIC!"

But it's not the same thing...
What we say and do are
Autistic behaviours, or

TRAITS.

Anyone can
have those, but
not just anyone can feel
how we experience and connect with the world. THAT
is what makes me Autistic, not the traits others see.

8

I'm very lucky to have friends who understand me. They aren't easy to find when you're Autistic... but the right ones are with you always!

Autism isn't an illness. My brain just works differently. I am autistic. I am me. I am Mark.

THE NEURODIVERGENTS
AUTISM
AND
SENSORY PROCESSING
Real experiences of autistic children

WRITTEN BY- I.M.ORKWERD

Aera

Dedicated to all of us whose senses work too hard.
Shout out to us all!
But not too loud, because, you know... my ears...

My name is Aera and I'm Autistic.

That means I don't experience the world the same way other people do.

I can struggle with **SENSORY PROCESSING**
That means the things we experience with our senses
are different
to other
people.

My
senses
can be
really
sensitive.
Crowds are
hard, because everyone
is so close and there's so much to see and hear and
smell that my mind feels like it can't do so much...

...so it **STOPS** working altogether and I shut down.

2

Loud or high pitched noises hurt my ears. I use headphones to block out the sound so it doesn't overwhelm me...

...but I have AWESOME hearing. I can hear my baby sister the second she wakes up from 3 rooms away!

Light touches or tickles on my skin make all the hairs on my body stand up. It makes me feel like bugs are crawling all over me....

Firm grips and pressure, like handshakes or hugs feel much better. It's why weighted blankets feel so snuggly!

Spicy food, or food that has lumpy, sloppy or slimy textures make me shiver, and can be really hard to eat...

That's why I don't like soup. I prefer bland flavours and food that holds its shape when you bite into it.

Crunchy things are the best!

5

Certain things can smell a
lot stronger to me
than other people, which can
sometimes be distracting
or even make me feel sick.

But my sensitive
sense of smell makes me
a great helper when
Mum needs to find where
the weird smell in
the fridge is coming from.

6

Bright light hurts my eyes.
Even when it's
cloudy outside, it's like the
clouds are glowing. I
got these cool sunglasses so
I can be outside
without it hurting my eyes!

I have
really good eyesight,
though. I can
see further than
anyone else
in my whole family!

I like being inside. I like being alone. I can control what I see, hear, smell, touch and taste better. Some people say Autistics would rather be alone, but that's just not true.

We **CRAVE** connection, but we get scared that people won't like us. We don't WANT to be alone... but it is easier.

8

That's why my friends are so amazing. They help me find ways to cope with my over-excited senses. They don't have the same sensitivities that I do, because nobody does! I don't have to be alone to feel safe or comfortable... not with them.

Autism isn't an illness. My brain just works differently. I am Autistic. I am me. I am Aera.

9

THE NEURODIVERGENTS
AUTISM
COMFORT AND COPING
Real experiences of autistic children

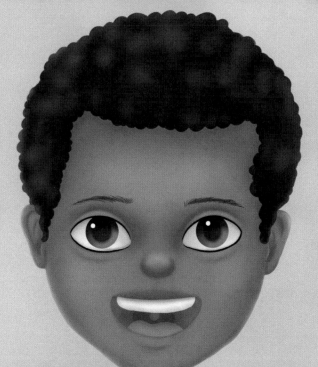

WRITTEN BY- I.M.ORKWERD

Jafari

Dedicated to the undiagnosed.
The ones who are struggling, unseen and unheard;
the ones who see themselves within these pages.
The ones whose time will come,
when at last they get the answers
that change their lives...
for the better.

My name is Jafari and
I'm Autistic.

That
means
I need
different types
of support
than other
people.

1

When I move in the same way over and over, it's called

STIMMING.

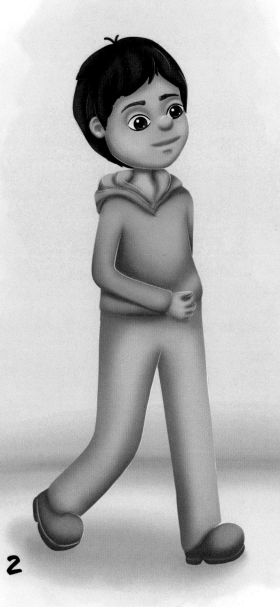

The familiar movement is comforting when I'm anxious or shows when I'm excited.

Other Autistics might click their fingers, or run their shoelaces through their hands just to feel the movement.

2

I like to move my body, especially my feet. I tap them when I'm sitting...

...wag them back and forth when I'm lying down...

...and when I'm standing up, I **WALK.**

3

I like to do things in the same way every time.

Having a routine or a schedule means I always know what's going to happen next, which helps keep me calm.

People know to tell me if something new is going to happen a long time before...

JANUARY 2022

TUESDAY	WEDNESDAY	THURSDAY	FRIDAY	S
4	⑤ ZURI'S BIRTHDAY PARTY. 11am-2pm.	6	7	8
			SOCCER	
11	12 PAEDIATRICIAN APPOINTMENT	13	14	
19	20	21		

...so I can enjoy them easier when they come!

5

People often label Autistics based on how well we cope. They can call us

HIGH FUNCTIONING or LOW FUNCTIONING

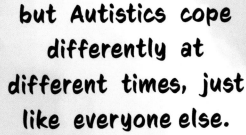

but Autistics cope differently at different times, just like everyone else.

People think I need medicine for my Autistic traits, but Autism doesn't work like that. There IS no medicine that can change the way my brain understands and interacts with the world.

I can function my best when I follow my routines, when I feel comfortable stimming and when I feel safe with the people around me.

But if things aren't feeling right, or something unexpected or distressing happens, I can be quite low functioning too.

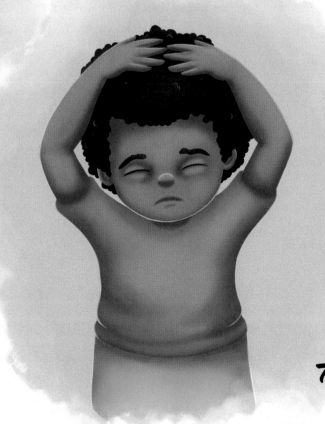

7

If I get overwhelmed, I'll stop talking and can't look people in the eyes, because I'm struggling to put my thoughts into words.

That's why labels make things hard. If people think I'm high functioning, they expect me to be ALL the time.

8

That's why I choose to be friends with people who love and accept me. I can have high days and low days, but they are there for me no matter what!

Autism isn't an illness.
My brain just works differently.
I am Autistic. I am me. I am Jafari.

Other books in the series

THE NEURODIVERGENTS
AUTISM
AND COMMUNICATION
Real experiences of autistic children

WRITTEN BY- I.M.ORKWERD
Mark

THE NEURODIVERGENTS
AUTISM
AND SENSORY PROCESSING
Real experiences of autistic children

WRITTEN BY- I.M.ORKWERD
Aera

THE NEURODIVERGENTS
AUTISM
COMFORT AND COPING
Real experiences of autistic children

WRITTEN BY- I.M.ORKWERD
Jafari

THE NEURODIVERGENTS
AUTISM
AND RELATIONSHIPS
Real experiences of autistic children

WRITTEN BY- I.M.ORKWERD
Zuri